Dedicated to my precious little mermaids,
Alli Mae and Ella.
You prove to the world everyday that you are
stronger than you appear and wiser than your years.
Thank you for being you, because you do it so well.
I love you to the moon, over the rainbow, and back!

-Papa

Published in 2021 by The Rainbow Lighthouse

ISBN 978-0-578-83936-3
Library of Congress Number 2021900793

Written by Erik Alexander
Illustrated by Victoria Zemke

For more info please visit,
www.nolapapa.com

Printed in the United States of America

The Adventures of Addie Underwater ©

Every Family is Built with Love

Written by: Erik Alexander
Illustrated by: Victoria Zemke

Addie the mermaid and her sister, Birdie, just woke up from their afternoon nap when Addie called out to her parents.

Daddy and Papa came quickly to their room.

"I was wondering... why do I have two daddies?"
Addie asked curiously.

Daddy and Papa looked at each other and smiled.

Papa replied, "Well Angelfish, all families are different."

Daddy added, "That's right! You are EXTRA special because you not only have one daddy, you have a Daddy AND a Papa!"

Papa replied, "Some families have a mommy and a daddy. Some families have just a mommy."

"And ya' know what? Some families have two mommies!" Daddy added.

"Are we all loved the same?" asked Addie.

"Absolutely!" Papa said, "Families may look different, but every family loves their mer-children the same."

"Do other families like to play games like we do?" Addie asked curiously.

Daddy responded, "Of course they do, Angelfish. Other families also like to play hide and go seek in the coral reefs. They even like to play Marco Polo with the other mermaids and merboys."

"And capture the seashell too, Papa?!" Addie and Birdie both asked excitedly.

"Yes they do, girls, they definitely do!"
Daddy reassured them both.

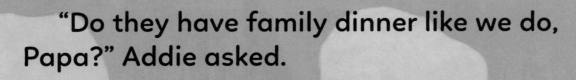

"Do they have family dinner like we do, Papa?" Addie asked.

"Oh baby, family dinner is important to everyone. But for some families, it is hard to eat together because some parents have to work." Papa answered.

"Some mamas, papas, mommies, and daddies have jobs that sometimes take up much of their time. Even though we can't have a family dinner all the time, we all wish with all of our heart that we could." Daddy reassured her.

"So you see, all families are different. And you know what, Starfish?" Papa asked. "Some families are different colors too!"

"You mean like a RAINBOW?!"

Addie asked excitedly.

Daddy and Papa eagerly replied, "Would you like to see?"

Addie and Birdie both screamed with excitement!

"Let's go get your baby brother and we will show you!" Daddy said.

Before their adventure up, Papa added, "Families are all different, but the love they have for their children shines just as bright as a rainbow!"

Addie and her family then left their cavern and began to swim to the surface.

They each poke their head out of the water.

Addie and Birdie both smile from ear to ear, because

there in the sky above them was the most beautiful...

Thank you to my best friend, soulmate, and husband, Douglas.
Thank you for your patience even when I am super intense.
I love you.

Thank you to our loving and supportive friends and family who love us
unconditionally. You know who you are.

Thank you to BSA Photography for capturing the most special moments
in our lives and creating the most amazing timeline of events I could
have ever dreamed of.

And last but certainly not least, thank you to New Orleans.
Your insurmountable beauty is the most breathtakingly perfect
backdrop to raise our family. Your stunning architecture and rich
culture inspires me every single day.
I love you more than red beans and rice.

Erik Alexander is a lifestyle writer and children's book author whose focus is on same sex families. His work has been published across the globe in various publications, outlets, magazines, websites, and social media platforms. Erik feels strongly that gay families deserve a voice just as any other family. Representation matters. It is crucial to teach children to recognize similarities in the love that all families have for each other, despite what differences they may have. These babies will help change the world and it is up to everyone to help pave the way for that to happen. Everyone should be able to have the coveted American dream. Erik feels it is his calling to help normalize the stigma behind what a family should look like regardless of sexual orientation or skin color. Family is family and love should be unconditional. Erik and his family live Uptown in New Orleans.

Victoria Zemke is an artist and entrepreneur from New Orleans, Louisiana. She is a lover of all things bright and colorful, and uses the vibrancy of her city as inspiration for her art. She has experience in graphic design, painting, and illustration. In 2018, Victoria started her business, Home Sweet NOLA, and in 2020 released a coloring book of her illustrations titled, *Coloring the Crescent City*. As a member of the LGBTQ+ community, Victoria is proud to be part of a book that represents diversity and same-sex families.

The Adventures of Addie Underwater is a five part children's book series, with the objective of tackling difficult questions and prompting important dialogue between parents and their children. Follow along with Addie and discover what she learns about family diversity, adoption, skin color, the loss of a family member, and dealing with bullies.

For more information or to purchase, please visit

www.nolapapa.com

Make sure to check out how you can help get these books in libraries across America!

Let's be friends!
Follow Addie on Instagram to get updates on her newest adventures

@adventures_of_addie_underwater

CPSIA information can be obtained
at www.ICGtesting.com
Printed in the USA
LVHW071332090521
686918LV00011B/194